P9-EKR-326

Bee is telling Phonic about
Inky. Inky is not feeling well
and Bee has sent her to bed.

Bee peeps into the bedroom
and sees Inky asleep. She looks
again. Inky has big red spots.

Ding dong! Here is Snake.
He has come to visit Inky.
Bee looks at Snake and
then at Snake's spots, and
will not let him in.

"You have given Inky your spots!" Bee tells Snake. "She is not feeling well at all."

"Er, Bee," interrupts Phonic, "I think you had better look in the mirror."

"I have got spots too!" Bee cries.

Snake and Phonic send Bee to bed as well. Then Snake brings hot drinks for Inky and Bee.

Next morning, Doctor
West visits the house
to see Inky and Bee.

Snake tells Doctor West about the spots, and that Bee thinks she and Inky got them from him.

Doctor West looks at Inky
and Bee, and then at
Snake. They *all* have spots.

Snake has spots on his spots!
"I am glad *I* cannot get
spots," thinks Phonic.

Doctor West tells Bee and
Inky that they did not get
the spots from Snake, and
that they will soon be better.

Inky's and Bee's spots will
all vanish, but Snake will
have some spots forever.